Ain't love grand!

That's magic!

C000157535

Hey! That's my carrot...

Beep, beep!

£6.99

BUGS AND FRIENDS
ANNUAL 2006

Hi! Welcome to the Bugs and Friends Annual. Inside you'll find loads of crazy activities and I'll tell you all about my latest adventures. So come on, toin the pages. I dare ya!

This book belongs to:

Name: .... Age: ....

Address: ....

....

Contents

CLUED UP!

Help Daffy work out what Bugs Bunny is saying by placing the toons in the grid. Write the shaded letters in the boxes to spell out Bugs Bunny's message.

DAFFY DUCK

PORKY PIG

SYLVESTER

WILE E COYOTE

YOSEMITE SAM

FOGHORN LEGHORN

ANSWERS ON PAGE 60

IT'S A-MAZE-ING!

START

Guide Bugs through the maze to rescue Lola Bunny.

ANSWER ON PAGE 60

BANGKOK BUNNY

WB 220

Writer: Jack Enyart   Artist: George Wildman   Letterer: Bob Pinaha   Colorist: Dave Tanguay

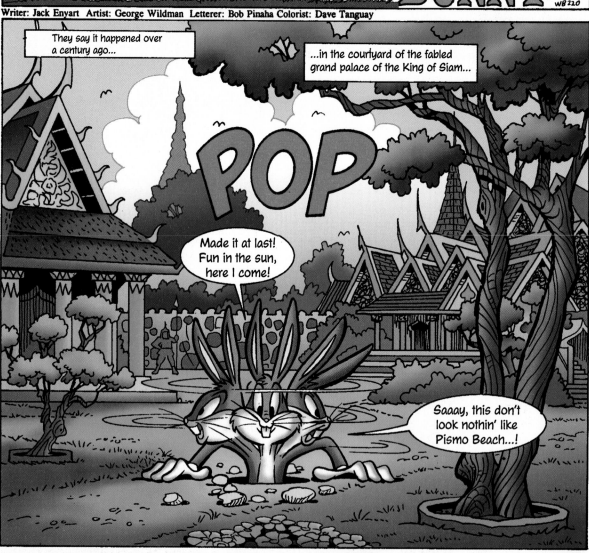

They say it happened over a century ago...

...in the courtyard of the fabled grand palace of the King of Siam...

POP

Made it at last! Fun in the sun, here I come!

Saaay, this don't look nothin' like Pismo Beach...!

That toin at Albuquerque throws me, every time!

What is this place anyways? Looks like some sorta amusement park...

To your duties, men!

You, apprentice guard! You stay...

TROMP   TROMP

I must impress on you the importance of guarding the compound on this of all days--

--our Great King's birthday!

Y-yes Captain!

Someday, I won't be an appwentice. Then we'll see who orders who awound!

You, pay attention!

Those street thieves were just caught sneaking in! Trying to steal Royal Treasure...

Gripe!

Grumble!

Mumble!

...No one, but no one must intrude today!

STAND GUARD!

I will stand! Stiff and wigid...

Hmmm.

...wigid as wood!

MAP

Say, doc. Y'think I should get back on the toinpike at Anaheim, Azusa... or Cucamonga?

?!

A wabbit! A wabbit on the Woyal gwounds!

"Royal grounds," huh?

I dunno. I woulda called the place "Funland", or somethin'!

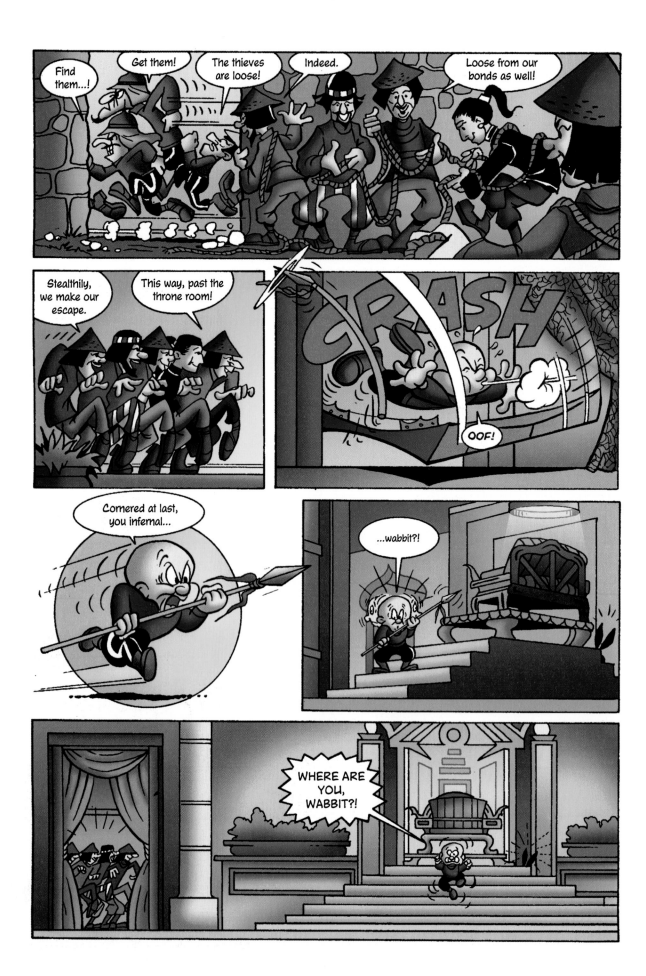

But I can tip th' balance, here...

Gwacious!

CRASH

The King...!

Where'd he go?

There! After him!

Run, pal. As fast as your thongs can carry ya!

Th-they're after me! But why?

You've been mistaken for someone important!

That's a mistake all wight!

This way...!

We'll hide in these!

Good idea! They're onwy fired once a year...

...I'm vewy gwateful. But why help me...?

Ehhh. Lets just say ya remind me of someone back home!

CRASH

...must come down.

THUD THUD

Oof! Not always so hard, though!

You two! How dare you keep the audience waiting?!

Time for performance. NOW!

B-but, we're not...

NOW!

"Now" is good.

Fine by us!

Attention! Attention, loyal subjects of His Majesty...

...the evening festival begins!

BOOINNG

We present in the King's honor a classic Siamese dance:

CONTINUED ON PAGE 20

FESTIVE FROLICS!

Bugs and the gang have been making a snowman. Can you spot the 10 differences between these two pictures?

ANSWERS ON PAGE 60

DAFFY DISGUISE!

Check out this groovy 3-D Daffy Duck mask! Have a go at making one yourself by following these simple steps.

1 Blow up a balloon and cover one side of it with four or five layers of torn newspaper and glue. Leave to dry.

2 Draw Daffy's beak onto thick card and cut it out. Use scrunched-up kitchen paper and PVA glue to pad it out and give a 3-D look.

Always ask an adult for help when using sharp objects!

3 Once the newspaper is dry, pop the balloon and cut a hole to slot the beak into. Fix it in place with sticky tape. Next add eyebrows and spiky hair using kitchen paper and glue, then cover with another layer of newspaper and glue. Leave to dry.

4

Cut eye holes and paint Daffy black, with white eyes and an orange beak.

5

When the paint is dry, cut the top off a pair of black tights and glue this inside the top of the mask. Leave to dry. To wear the mask, simply put the tights on your head!

CONTINUED FROM PAGE 16

"The King..."

BOOT

"...and the dancing girl!"

"Once a beautiful girl was brought before our King...

"... to dance, in hopes she might please him.

"But the King was not easily pleased."

Uh-oh. Stage fright!

Ahem. "The King was not easily pleased!"

BUMP

UNH!

He was serious...

"... scowling...

"... and stern!

"But the dancer was determined.

YIPES...!

Those guys, again! Gotta wind this up quick somehow...

LOOK!

THE KING

ON STAGE!

"And finally she was blessed, with his Majesty's approval."

Yes! I am pleased!

Really? Oooh, I'm sooo glad!

SMACK

GET HIM!

That's all, folks!

OW!

?

I feel quite flushed...

Out like lights, all of 'em. A poifect score!

...woyally flushed!

HURRAH!

What a production for the King's birthday!

But, it's not over till it's over!

Stop! Welease me! What's this all about?!

About you impersonating His Majesty, the King...

A grave offense!

You cursed cwitter. This is all your fault.

Wish I was lyin' on Pismo Beach right now!

Uh-oh. We weally are in deep twouble...

THRONE ROOM

...they're taking us to the thwone room!

All bow before His Royal Highness, The King of Siam!

Lower, wabbit, lower!

Hey! Only an idiot could mistake you for this guy...

...he doesn't look anything like you, doc!

EXACTLY SO!

He will be rewarded for his bravery, and made apprentice Captain of the guards!

As for you, long-eared one...

The King was generous with Bugs, too!

More hot-and-spicy carrots?

Don't see why not.

I tell ya... it's the only way to travel!

PISMO BEACH

THE END

LOONEY QUIZ!

Test your looney knowledge of toon trivia with this quick quiz. Check your answers on page 60.

1 Who likes hunting 'wabbits'?

....

2 Which toon chases Road Runner?

....

3 Who says "Eh, what's up, Doc?"

....

4 Who is this?

....

5 What does Bugs like to munch?

6 What type of animal is Tweety?

TRUE OR FALSE ROUND!

7 Taz is a dog

T F

8 Tweety says "Thufferin' Thuccotash"

T F

9 Daffy Duck has a red beak

T F

10 Elmer Fudd wears a hat

T F

11 Marvin's loyal companion is called K-9

T F

12 This is Pepe Le Pew

T F

SWEET SAVERS!

Have a go at making these fantastic, fun jars to store your favourite sweets.

1

Always ask an adult for help when using sharp objects!

Draw around the base of a jam jar onto card and cut it out. Cut a strip 3cm wide and long enough to go around the circle of card. Fix in place with sticky tape to make the base of your sweetie jar.

Roll up two pieces of card and fix onto the base to make legs. Add card feet to the end of the legs.

2

3 Fix a yoghurt pot to the jam jar lid and add two card ears to the top. Cut two arms from card. Cover each of the pieces individually with a layer or two of torn newspaper and glue.

4 Paint Bugs with grey, white and black paint. When dry, glue the base and arms onto your jar. Screw on the lid.

Why not make an Elmer Fudd jar in the same way? Instead of ears, just add a ball of kitchen paper to the top of the yoghurt pot with a card hat brim.

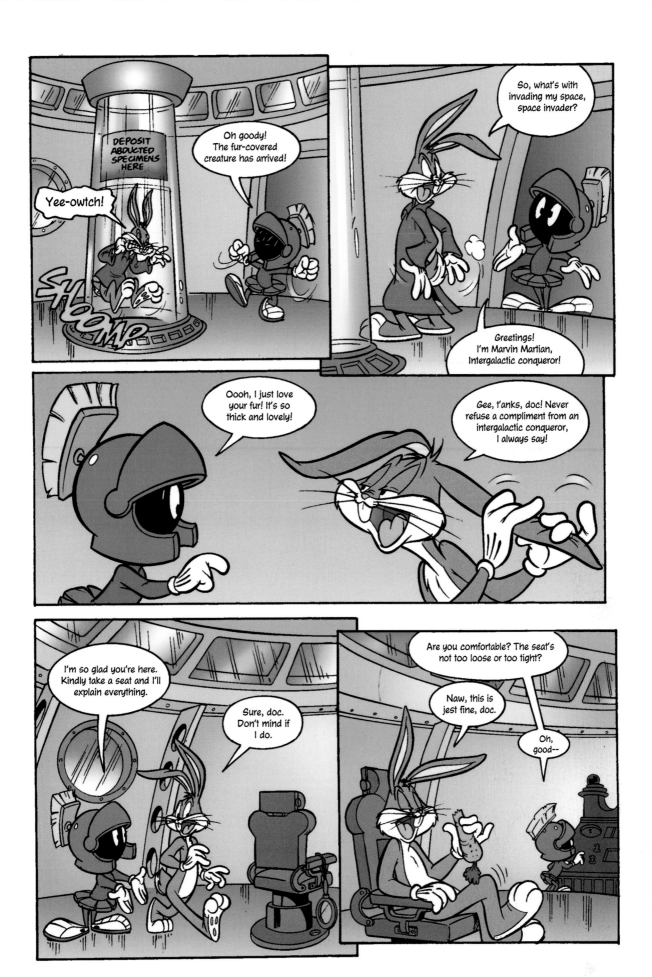

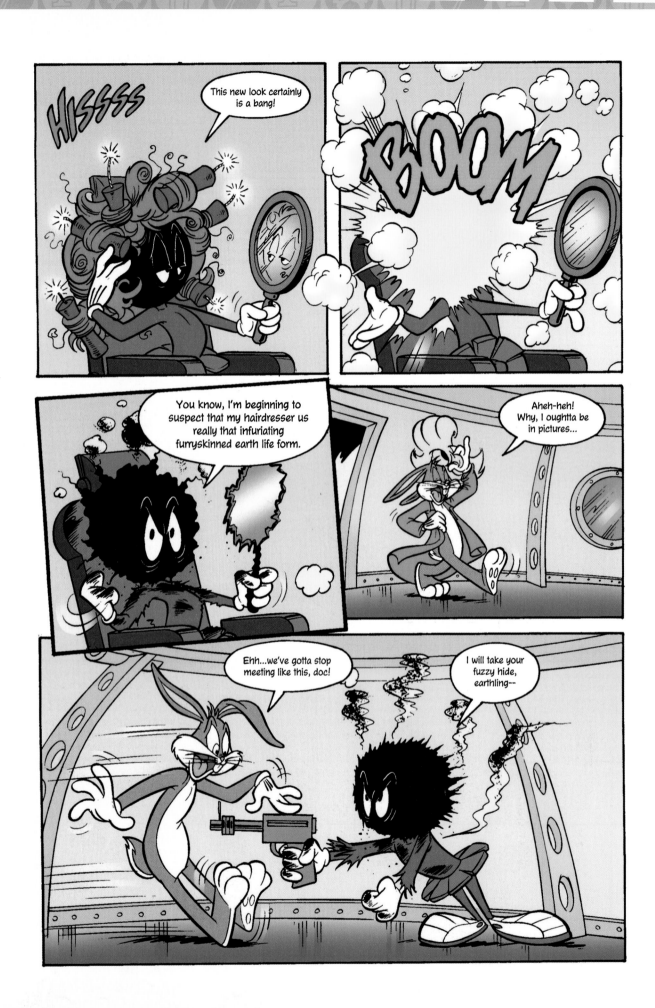

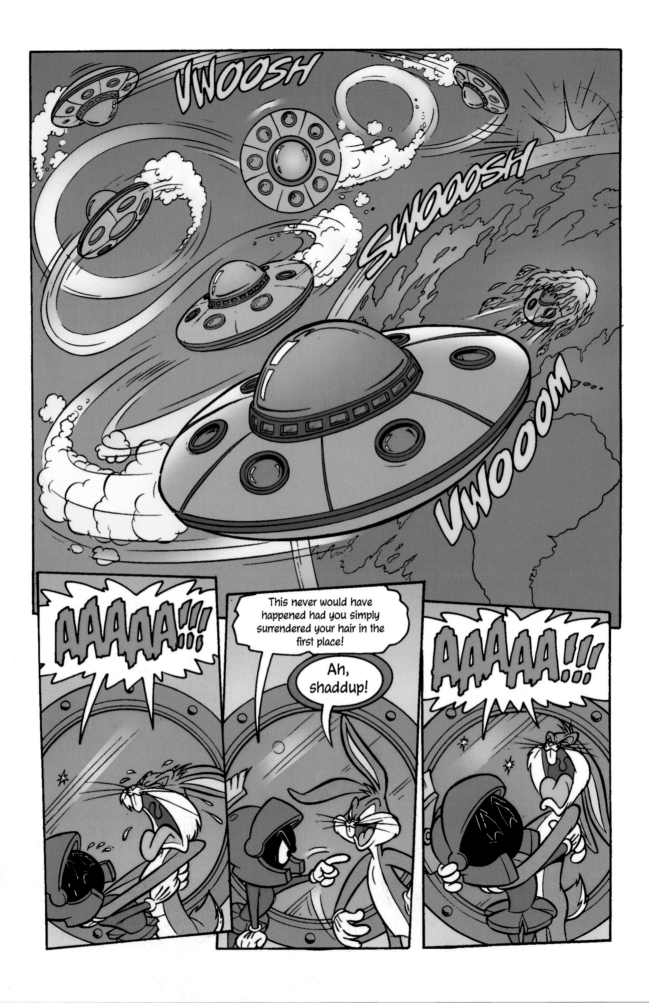

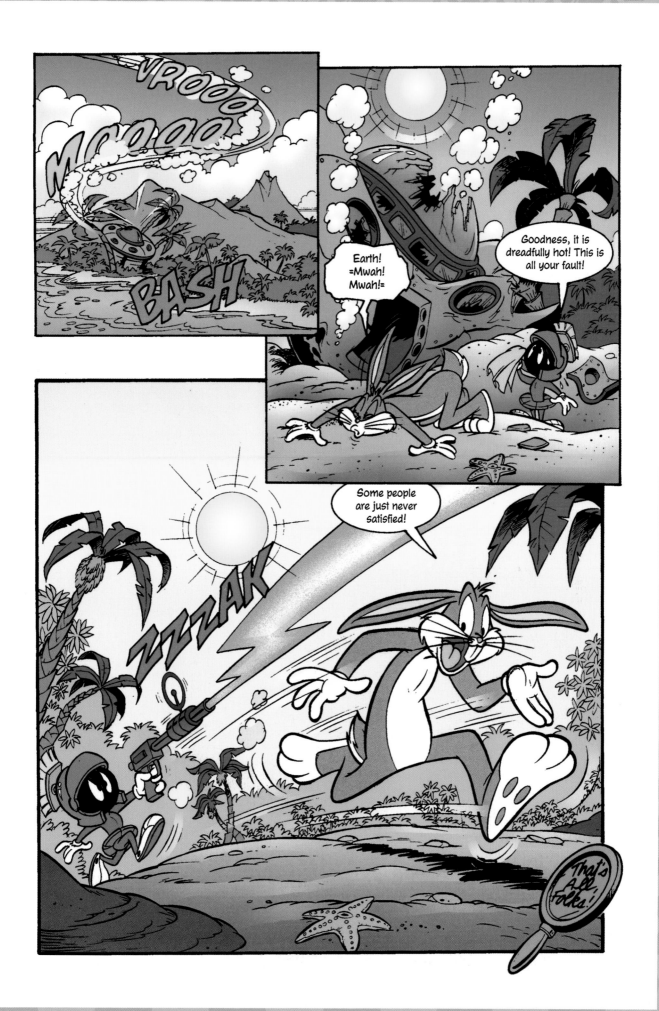

Ain't I a Masterpiece?

Use the grid on the right to draw Bugs Bunny then add some colour to create a masterpiece of your own!

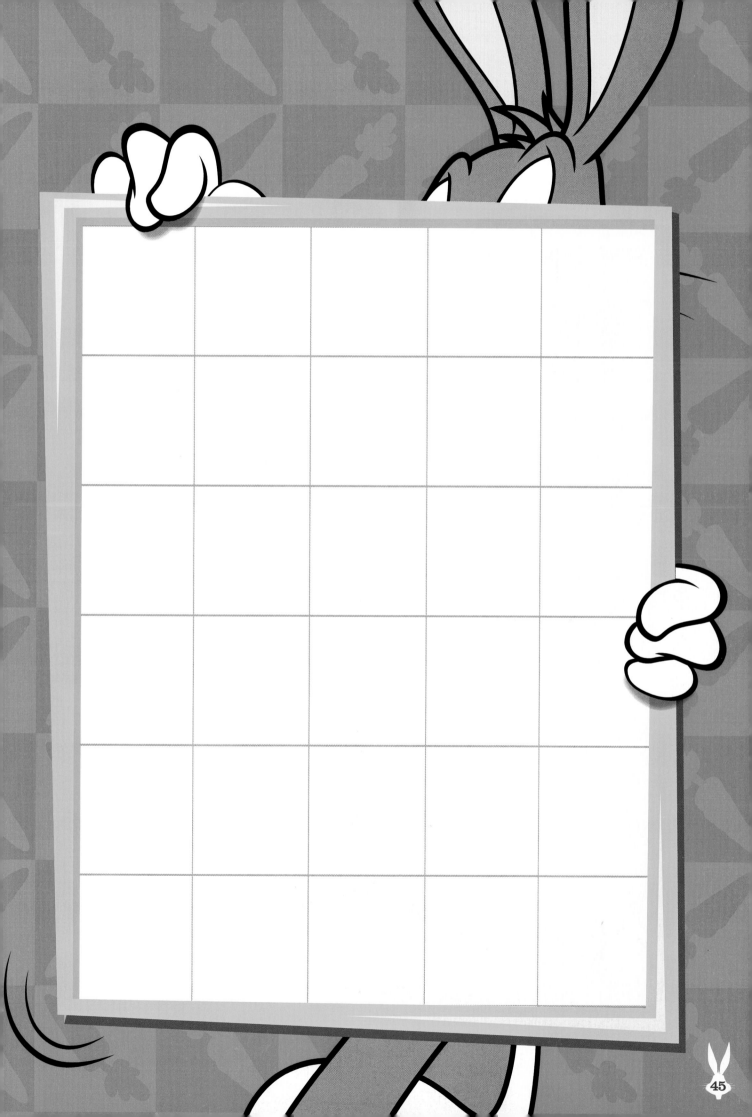

HARE-WAY TO HEAVEN

Writer: Michael Eury Penciller: Oscar Gonzales Loya Inker: Jim Amash Letterer: Bob Pinaha Colorist: Duendes del Sur

Floss me!

Eew!

Several strands of dental floss later...

Bugsy, since you're hoppin' to help me out, I've taken the liberty of makin' you a list of chores!

But, doc, I've got to get to the studio-- we start filmin' the new picture today!

Why, yes I am! And you said you were gonna be nice to me, didn't ya... pal?

Yeah, I did, didn't I? =sigh=

About that picture... I want you to call the director and tell him you're bowin' out. Passin' the part to me!

Say what?! Are you Daffy?!

Then call the director and quit! And just cause you're givin' up your part doesn't mean you aren't welcome at the studio, Bugs.

Be there at eleven-- to give me a pedicure!

Why...? Why...?

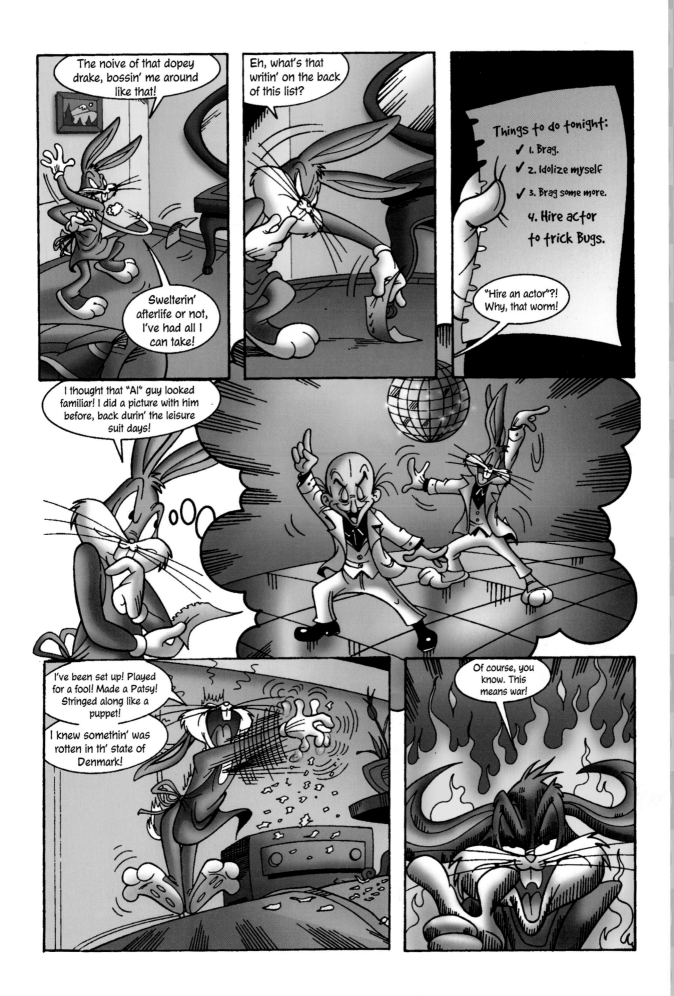

COMIC CAPERS!

Bugs and Daffy have out-witted Elmer Fudd again! Add a splash of colour to bring the picture to life.

SHAPE SHIFTING!

Can you spot which shadow matches Bugs' pose on the left?

A   B   C   D   E

ANSWER
(See below)

ANSWER

P6 CLUED UP

F
Y O S E M I T E S A M
G   D
H   A
P O R K Y P I G   F
O   S   W   F
R   Y   I   Y
N   L   L   D
L   V   E   U
E   E   C   C
G   S   O   K
H   T   Y
O   E   O
R   R   T
N   E

WHAT'S UP DOC?

P7 IT'S A-MAZE-ING

P17 FESTIVE FROLICS

P29 LOONEY QUIZ

1. Elmer Fudd
2. Wile E Coyote
3. Bugs Bunny
4. Taz
5. Carrots
6. A bird
7. False
8. False
9. False
10. True
11. True
12. True

P60 SHAPE SHIFTING

The answer is D

Bedazzled Daffy

Go Porky!

Smokin'

I'm gonna get you...